GOOD HOUSEKEEPING

Home

L O G   B O O K

OCTOPUS/EBURY PRESS

Published by Octopus Books Limited
59 Grosvenor Street
London W1X 9DA

and

Ebury Press
National Magazine House
72 Broadwick Street
London W1V 2BP

First impression 1985

Compiled by Cassandra Kent, Consumer Affairs Editor, Good Housekeeping

Designed by Peter Bridgewater Associates
Illustrated by Annie Ellis

ISBN 086 273 272 7
Filmset by Advanced Filmsetters (Glasgow) Ltd

Printed and bound in Italy

When you first buy this book it's wise to study it thoroughly and take time to fill in all the necessary information. In terms of the hours you will save in the future by knowing where to find vital information about the house, it will be time well spent.

When you have filled in all the details necessary in this book you will have a unique record of your home and its contents, what it costs to run and what improvements you have made to it.

You also have information to make life easier on a daily basis. This includes advice on coping with emergencies of all kinds – from personal injury to stain removal – telephone numbers for virtually all household contingencies, lists of the people who service and repair items in your home and of your favourite shops. You also have a set of useful tips for making life around your home easier, quicker or cheaper.

A PERMANENT RECORD

Should you want to sell your home you will have at your fingertips all the information a potential purchaser is likely to need. The necessary facts and figures on fuel consumption, rates, decorating costs and insulation will all be logged together.

Contents

Inventory of Contents

You probably think you know what you own in terms of possessions. But if you were burgled it could well take months before you remembered everything that had disappeared. For this reason, it's a good idea to keep an inventory of your belongings. It's not just helpful in the event of their being stolen but it is also helpful when it comes to working out their values for your household contents insurance (see page 51). You can either just keep one list of items or in addition log either what they cost originally or what their current replacement value is. Alternatively, you may prefer to keep this information somewhere else where it won't be seen by other people.

LOGGING THE CONTENTS OF EACH ROOM

Take your time when you itemize the contents of each room and bear in mind that you should list fixed as well as movable items and also the regular contents of drawers and cupboards. Don't just list those things which are valuable now. Nothing comes down in price and the cost of replacing a lot of relatively inexpensive items which have been stolen or damaged by flood or fire can soon mount up.

When listing items which are moved from room to room (e.g., a portable television or trolley), log them down in the room in which they spend most time.

With electrical items such as hi-fi equipment, video cassette recorders, kitchen appliances and so on, make a note of the serial number (you find it on the rating plate which is usually on the base of the machine) as this is helpful when tracing stolen goods or ordering spare parts needed for repair.

PHOTOGRAPHING VALUABLES

With items such as treasured pictures or ornaments it is a good idea to keep a photograph as this helps recovery if they are stolen. There is no need to have pictures taken professionally; you can snap the things yourself with an ordinary camera (Polaroid is ideal).

Do not record details of decoration on these two pages; they should be listed in the home decorating record on pages 72 to 95.

Living Room Inventory

FURNITURE	CARE NOTES

Living Room Inventory

FURNITURE	CARE NOTES

CARE NOTES

Dining Room Inventory

FURNITURE AND ACCESSORIES	NOTES ON CARE

Kitchen Inventory

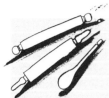

Most of the equipment in your kitchen will be listed on the following pages. Note here details of your kitchen units including manufacturer's name and address, the name of the range and the address of the installer (where appropriate). You may wish at some future date to add extra cupboards or to replace doors or drawers.

Kitchen Equipment List

The point of keeping a list of your kitchen equipment is to enable you to replace items destroyed by fire or flood. While individually many of the items are of little monetary value, taken together they mount up to a sum which you would certainly want to claim off an insurance company. The list is also a useful aide mémoire when it comes to re-equipping or replacing worn out equipment.

Use the boxes in this list to tick items you have in your kitchen. Where you have more than one of a particular item, e.g., wooden spoons, make a note of how many you have in the box.

Milk pan ☐
Omelette pan ☐
Pie dish ☐
Pie dish ☐
Preserving pan ☐
Pressure cooker ☐
Ring mould ☐
Roasting tin(s) ☐
Sandwich tin (size) ☐
Sandwich tin (size) ☐
Saucepan (volume) ☐
Saucepan (volume) ☐
Saucepan (volume) ☐
Saucepan (volume) ☐
Saucepan (volume) ☐
Saucepan (volume) ☐
Soufflé dish ☐
Steamer/steaming basket ☐
Swiss roll tin ☐
Terrine ☐
Yorkshire pudding tin ☐

COOK AND BAKE WARE

Baking sheet ☐
Baking sheet(s) ☐
Bun tin ☐
Bun tin ☐
Casserole – (volume) ☐
Casserole – (volume) ☐
Casserole – (volume) ☐
Casserole – (volume) ☐
Chip pan with basket ☐
Deep cake tin (size) ☐
Deep cake tin (size) ☐
Double saucepan ☐
Egg poacher ☐
Flan dish ☐
Frying pan ☐
Gratin dish ☐
Loaf tin (size) ☐
Loaf tin (size) ☐

COOK AND BAKE ACCESSORIES

Carving dish ☐
Colander ☐
Cooling rack ☐
Dripping pot ☐
Measuring jug ☐
Meat thermometer ☐
Microwave probe ☐
Mixing bowl (size) ☐
Mixing bowl (size) ☐
Oven thermometer ☐
Pan trivet ☐
Pie plate ☐
Pudding basin (size) ☐
Pudding basin (size) ☐
Pudding basin (size) ☐

BASIC UTENSILS (NON-ELECTRICAL)

Airtight storage containers ☐
Balloon whisk ☐
Basting spoon ☐
Biscuit and pastry cutters ☐
Bottle opener ☐
Box grater ☐
Bread board ☐
Bread knife ☐
Can opener ☐
Carving knife and fork ☐
Chip cutter ☐
Chopping board ☐
Citrus squeezer ☐
Colander ☐
Cook's knife ☐
Corkscrew ☐
Fish slice ☐
Flour dredger ☐
Garlic press ☐
Ice cream scoop ☐
Jelly/blancmange mould ☐
Knife sharpener ☐
Ladle ☐
Measuring spoons ☐
Mincer ☐
Mortar and pestle ☐
Nutcrackers ☐
Palette knife ☐
Paring knife ☐
Pastry brush ☐
Pie funnel ☐
Piping bag and nozzles ☐
Potato masher ☐
Potato peeler ☐
Rolling pin ☐
Rotary whisk ☐
Salt and peppermills ☐
Scissors ☐
Sieve(s) (metal and nylon) ☐

Skewers ☐
Slotted spoon ☐
Spatula ☐
Tongs ☐
Wooden spatula ☐
Wooden spoon ☐

OPTIONAL EXTRAS

Apple corer ☐
Asparagus steamer ☐
Bean slicer ☐
Butter curler ☐
Ceramic baking beans ☐
Cherry stoner ☐
Eclair baking sheet ☐
Egg separator ☐
Egg slicer ☐
Fish kettle ☐
Fish scaler ☐
Griddle ☐
Herb mill ☐
Icing comb ☐
Icing ruler ☐
Icing turntable ☐
Jam or sweet thermometer ☐
Mandolin grater ☐
Melon baller ☐
Pasta maker ☐
Pastry blender ☐
Pastry board ☐
Pastry crimper ☐
Potato baker ☐
Poultry scissors ☐
Ramekin dishes ☐
Salad shaker ☐
Skimmer ☐
Spaghetti server ☐
Spring-release cake tin ☐
Waffle iron ☐
Wok ☐

Kitchen Appliances

When and where bought	Serial no.

Fill in the data above on each of your electric kitchen appliances. It will save you a great deal of time when servicing or repairs are needed.

Guaranteed until	Servicing agent	Location of instructions

Utility Room Inventory

FURNITURE AND ACCESSORIES (Including appliances)	NOTES ON CARE

Playroom / Study Inventory

FURNITURE AND ACCESSORIES	NOTES ON CARE

Bedrooms Inventory

FURNITURE AND ACCESSORIES	NOTES ON CARE

Bedrooms Inventory

FURNITURE AND ACCESSORIES	NOTES ON CARE

Bathrooms Inventory

FURNITURE AND ACCESSORIES	NOTES ON CARE

Cellar or Loft Inventory

Many people's lofts or cellars are used to store junk so it's useful to keep a list of what you have put in there to save fruitless scrabbling around when you want to find something. If you store wine in your cellar in any quantity it is sensible to keep a special cellar book or use our companion *Good Housekeeping Kitchen Log Book* to list type, vintage, quantity and 'drink by' dates.

NUMBER OF CELLAR KEY:

Garage Inventory

CONTENTS (Other than car)	NOTES ON USE/CARE

NUMBER OF GARAGE KEY:	LOCATION OF SPARE KEY:

Shed Inventory

CONTENTS	NOTES ON USE/CARE

NUMBER OF SHED KEY:

LOCATION OF SPARE KEY:

Sport and Leisure Checklist

Use these pages to list sport and leisure equipment that isn't a fixed item in a particular room. These items may include bicycles, exercise equipment, radios, portable television sets, video cassette recorder, cameras and other photographic equipment, computer and software, typewriter and so on. Note down their serial numbers (where appropriate), distinguishing marks and description. Obviously, a large television set or exercise bike stays put and should be logged where it is used.

China Checklist

China gets broken in even the best run homes so keep your stock replenished and throw out any cracked or chipped items which could harbour germs. If buying seconds, check each piece for flaws. Where space is limited consider storage; you may want a type that stacks well. Note that if you have a dishwasher you will need more china than when washing by hand; avoid designs with gilding which is damaged by dishwasher detergent.

You can also buy special cookware designed for use in microwave ovens. It is made from a variety of materials, all of which absorb less microwave energy than glass and china. This means that food will cook more quickly and evenly without hotspotting or sticking to the base. Choose only shapes which you know will be useful.

If you don't want to buy special microwave ware much household crockery can safely be used in a microwave oven provided it does not have any gilt or metal decoration. To test if it is suitable, fill with water and microwave on High for one minute. If the water is hot and the container is cool, it will work well in a microwave. If the water is hot and the container just warm it will work but not very efficiently as much of the microwave energy is being absorbed by the container. If the container is hot and the water only warm it is not suitable.

If you find that your particular range of china has been discontinued, you can try to match it up through one of the following services: *Chinamatch*, Nutwood, Fen Walk, Woodbridge, Suffolk (03943 3078), *China Matching Service*, Fern Lea, Frogmore, Kingsbridge, Devon

Name of range
Numbers of each type
Manufacturer's address
Stockists
Notes on care

Name of range
Numbers of each type
Manufacturer's address
Stockists
Notes on care

Name of range
Numbers of each type
Manufacturer's address
Stockists
Notes on care

Name of range
Numbers of each type
Manufacturer's address
Stockists
Notes on care

Name of range
Numbers of each type
Manufacturer's address
Stockists
Notes on care

Name of range
Numbers of each type
Manufacturer's address
Stockists
Notes on care

Name of range
Numbers of each type
Manufacturer's address
Stockists
Notes on care

Name of range
Numbers of each type
Manufacturer's address
Stockists
Notes on care

Name of range
Numbers of each type
Manufacturer's address
Stockists
Notes on care

China Checklist

Name of range
Numbers of each piece
Manufacturer's address
Stockists
Notes on care

Name of range
Numbers of each piece
Manufacturer's address
Stockists
Notes on care

Name of range
Numbers of each piece
Manufacturer's address
Stockists
Notes on care

Name of range
Numbers of each piece
Manufacturer's address
Stockists
Notes on care

Name of range
Numbers of each piece
Manufacturer's address
Stockists
Notes on care

Name of range
Numbers of each piece
Manufacturer's address
Stockists
Notes on care

Name of range
Numbers of each piece
Manufacturer's address
Stockists
Notes on care

Glass Checklist

Name of range
Numbers of each piece
Manufacturer's address
Stockists
Notes on care

Name of range
Numbers of each piece
Manufacturer's address
Stockists
Notes on care

Name of range
Number of pieces
Manufacturer's address
Stockists
Notes on care

Name of range
Number of pieces
Manufacturer's address
Stockists
Notes on care

Name of range
Number of pieces
Manufacturer's address
Stockists
Notes on care

Name of range
Number of pieces
Manufacturer's address
Stockists
Notes on care

It is probably not worth logging the everyday glasses you use. Sale bargains and special offers which have come when buying petrol – together with breakages – keep the total variable in most homes. High quality glass is both beautiful and valuable, so keep a list of that and remember to include cut glass bowls, vases and other pieces as well as actual glasses.

Cutlery Checklist

Name of range
Number of pieces
Manufacturer's address
Stockists
Notes on care

Name of range
Number of pieces
Manufacturer's address
Stockists
Notes on care

Name of range
Numbers of each type
Manufacturer's address
Stockists
Notes on care

Name of range
Numbers of each type
Manufacturer's address
Stockists
Notes on care

Name of range
Numbers of each type
Manufacturer's address
Stockists
Notes on care

Name of range
Numbers of each type
Manufacturer's address
Stockists
Notes on care

It's only too easy to lose odd items of cutlery by accidentally scraping them into a waste bin or down a disposal unit. When buying a complete set, always check where you can get replacement pieces. If you own a dishwasher, be sure that all the cutlery you buy is suitable for washing in it. Note that whether washed by hand or dishwasher *all* cutlery (whatever metal) benefits from cleaning with an appropriate polish.

Household Linen Checklist

Name of range
Numbers of each type
Manufacturer's address
Stockists
Notes on care

Name of range
Number of pieces
Manufacturer's address
Stockists
Notes on care

Name of range
Number of pieces
Manufacturer's address
Stockists
Notes on care

Name of range
Number of pieces
Manufacturer's address
Stockists
Notes on care

Name of range
Number of pieces
Manufacturer's address
Stockists
Notes on care

Name of range
Number of pieces
Manufacturer's address
Stockists
Notes on care

With household linen you get what you pay for. So fork out for long-life quality or opt for cheap and cheerful lines that can be replaced from time to time without extravagant outlay. Household linen gets fairly hard wear so the more you have and can use in rotation, the longer it will last
Remember that deep dyed fabrics tend to run.

Knowing About Electricity

Electricity plays an important part in most people's lives. It is used for light, heat, cooking and for powering an amazing number of small appliances, from blenders to hedge cutters. Nonetheless it must be used safely, carefully and economically.

Wiring should be checked regularly to ensure it is in good condition. Any home over 25 years old will probably need rewiring and if you are having the job done professionally, use a member of the Electrical Contractors' Association; your local Electricity Board will advise on members in your area.

Make sure your electrical circuit can cope with the demands you make on it. It is far better to turn single socket outlets into double ones than use an adaptor and possibly overload it. Replace frayed flexes immediately.

When buying new electrical products choose those which carry the BEAB (British Electro-technical Approvals Board) symbol which indicates that they have passed stringent safety tests. Choose products which conform to British Standards.

REDUCING THE BILLS

If your electricity bills seem high, consider how you can reduce them. Start by carrying out a home audit to see how many units you use each week and try to work out why. Auditing over a period of a few weeks will show you what things use more electricity – for example more meals cooked because the children are home half-term or heating bills higher because someone was ill in bed – and help you decide whether you would be wise to run some of your appliances on the Economy 7 tariff which is considerably cheaper than the normal day tariff. Your Electricity Board can supply details and the Electricity Consumers' Council has a leaflet which tells you how to organize a home audit.

Don't run your washing machine, dishwasher or tumble dryer unless you have a full load (or use the half load facility). Try to fill your oven with cook-ahead dishes rather than switching it on for just an individual meal.

The chart below shows the amount of use you can get from different appliances for one unit of electricity.

Blender	500 pints soup
Can opener	6,250 cans
Coffee percolator	75 cups
Electric underblanket	7 evenings
Extractor fan	24 hours
Fan heater	30 minutes (2 kW rating)
Hair dryer	3 hours
Hair rollers	22 treatments
Iron	2 hours
Kettle	12 pints
Power drill	4 hours
Radio	20 hours
Shaver	1,800 shaves
Stereo	8–10 hours
TV (colour)	6 hours
Toaster	70 slices
Tumble dryer	30 minutes
Vacuum cleaner	2 hours

Electric Sockets

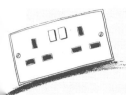

You can use this page to note down how many electric socket outlets there are in each room and whether they are single or double. Singles can usually be changed to doubles very easily. Sockets are locked into one or more ring mains which can usually sustain up to 30 amps of electricity. Since you are unlikely to require this amount at any one time it is possible to fit sockets for maximum con-venience in terms of heat and light. Cooker and water heating circuits, which use a lot of electricity, are always wired separately. If you wish to turn off electricity at the mains when you are away from home but want to leave a freezer running, have it put on a separate circuit.

It is useful to have this information so that you can work out whether you will overload a ring main if you add extra socket outlets and also work out where you can run new electrical appliances.

ROOM

SOCKETS

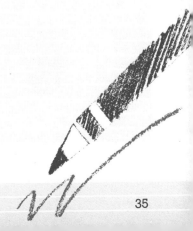

Electricity Bill Record

Use these pages to log details of your electricity bills so that you can compare them from season to season and year to year. If there are any serious discrepancies, without your having changed your pattern of usage, it is then an easy matter to make a check with the electricity board.

There are various ways of paying your electricity bill if you don't want to pay it in one lump. You can arrange a special account with your bank so that they pay the bills when they come in, buy fuel stamps at the post office or electricity board showroom each week and stick them on a special card to be used to pay all or part of the bill when it comes. Or you can have a meter put in your home and feed it with coins as and when necessary. Bear in mind, though, that this latter course works out more expensive than the previous two. If you are of a thrifty turn of mind, you can pay money into a high interest building society account and earn interest on it while waiting to pay your bill.

DATE OF READING/ESTIMATE

UNITS USED	AMOUNT PAID	NOTES

Wiring Plan

It is a big help if you know where your electric wiring runs behind the walls so that you can avoid cutting through it when doing replastering or hanging pictures or in case you want to extend the circuit at any time.

If you are having your home rewired ask the electrician to tell you exactly where the wires run and make a plan of them on these two pages. Otherwise, use the space to note where you know that wires run.

Wiring

Living room

Kitchen

Dining room

Playroom/study

Bathroom

Bedroom(s)

Utility room

Garage

Shed

Cellar/loft

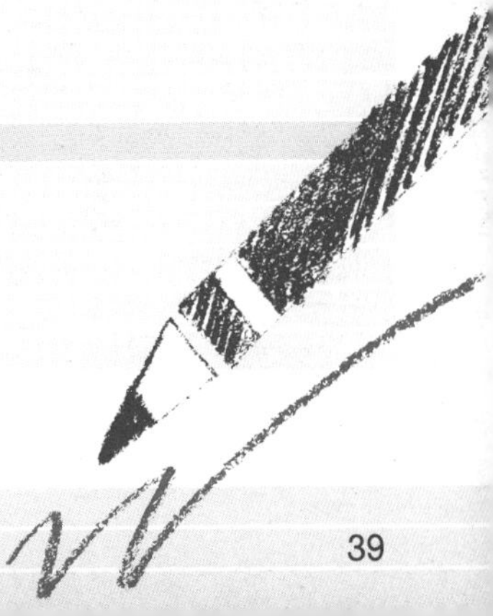

Knowing About Gas

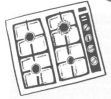

Gas can be dangerous and even a competent handyman should never attempt to deal with leaks or other problems. Always call in a qualified gas service engineer to install and repair any appliances and/or in the case of an emergency. Ring the number of British Gas service in your local telephone directory.

When using gas appliances you must always ensure adequate air ventilation as gas needs air to burn safely. If you suspect a gas leak, turn off the supply at the meter to try to stop it and call gas service immediately. Do not turn the gas on again until the leak has been dealt with. British Gas does not charge for checking for leaks nor for the first 30 minutes of making your gas supply safe although they may disconnect the supply temporarily if they cannot deal with the problem quickly.

KEEPING AN EYE ON THE BILLS

If you think your gas bills are too high you should carry out a weekly gas audit to see exactly how much you are using and try and pinpoint where you could cut back. For example, do your children get home from school and immediately turn up the heating? Are you using the oven for long periods with only a little food in it? Does hot water take up a large part of the cost and should you therefore install a shower which uses

considerably less? Check, too, that your insulation is adequate around the home (see also page 50). A leaflet telling you how to check your weekly gas costs and register them on a graph is available from the *National Gas Consumers' Council*, 4th Floor, 162/8 Regent Street, London W1R 5TB.

CHANGING TO GAS

If you want to go on to the gas supply and live within 25 yards of a suitable gas main, British Gas must normally supply you but it can charge you for laying and maintaining any pipe on your land and for any further length of pipe between your land and the main in excess of 10 yards. British Gas is responsible for your gas supply up to the point where the pipe joins the meter and for the meter itself. The maintenance and safety of the appliances and supply in your home are your responsibility.

British Gas is entitled to enter your property to read, inspect or attend to the meter or the gas supply pipes. You, as householder, should always ask to see the identity card carried by all British Gas employees.

Where the Pipes Run

Make a note on this page of where your gas pipes run and where there are any joints or taps that you might need to direct a repairer to in the event of a leak or fault. You can also note down details too of any gas appliances you have (e.g., room or water heaters) together with a note of where you keep the operating instructions.

Gas Bill Record

Use these pages to log details of your gas bills so that you can compare them from season to season and year by year. If there are any serious discrepancies, without your having changed your pattern of usage, then it is an easy matter to make a check with the gas board.

There are various ways of paying your gas bill if you don't want to pay it in one lump. You can arrange a special account with your bank so that they pay the bills when they come in, buy fuel stamps at the post office or gas board showroom each week and stick them on a special card to be used to pay all or part of the bill when it comes. If you are of a thrifty turn of mind, you can pay money into a high interest building society account and earn interest on it while waiting to pay your bill.

DATE OF READING/ESTIMATE

UNITS USED	AMOUNT PAID	NOTES

Central Heating

Central heating can be expensive to run so make sure your system is as efficient as possible. You should always call in expert advice if putting in a new system and if you inherit an old one that doesn't seem to work effectively, pay for an expert to advise you about how it can be improved without complete replacement. Fitting high output radiators in place of standard ones which aren't doing a good job in rooms which need a lot of heat is one solution and fitting individual thermostats to radiators will enable you to regulate the temperature in different rooms more finely. You could put a floor which is not used extensively on to a separate zone control that keeps the chill off but does not heat. It might be that moving the thermostat out of the draught from the front door would keep the house warmer provided, of course, that you already have or install good insulation (page 50).

If you are installing central heating in a home for the first time check with your local authority if you are eligible for a grant. Otherwise, you may be able to pay for it by topping up your mortgage or by acquiring a home improvement loan from your bank. Also you can check with your local gas board to see if they will arrange special credit terms.

Use this space for details of your central heating boiler and servicing arrangements.

BOILER BRAND MODEL NO.

SERVICED ON (DATE)

REPAIRED ON (DATE)

NOTES

COST

Radiator Details

Here you can write down details of each central heating radiator in your home. List its size, location, whether single or double, whether it has an individual thermostat fitted (if so, which type and where the instructions for it are kept). Note the dates when you paint radiators and any particular problems on any one radiator (e.g., spurts when you bleed it).

Central Heating Pipes

Use these pages to draw out a plan of where the central heating pipes run and then mark down where there are joins and valves so that you know which floorboards to take up in the event of problems. If you have a new system fitted and haven't yet laid flooring, paint indelible lines on the floor showing exactly where the pipes run.

Central Heating Bill Record

It may not be possible to separate out your central heating costs from your other electricity or gas costs. But if your system runs on oil or solid fuel use these pages to list delivery dates, quantities and costs. Otherwise use them for extra household information you may wish to record.

Knowing About Insulation

Good insulation is the vital key to keeping down heating bills, whatever fuel you use. Some forms of insulation, such as lagging the hot water tank, are cheap and very effective; others cost considerably more and in terms of paying for themselves, take considerably longer.

You can sometimes get a local council grant for insulating your loft or for topping up existing insulation to a more effective level. Ask your local authority about this and remember that if you are applying for a grant for new insulation, you should not start work until it has been approved. Otherwise, you will need to raise the cash yourself. For expensive insulation like double glazing you may be able to extend your mortgage, or get a home improvement loan or finance house arrangement; shop around for the best terms available.

Insulate the hot water tank by wrapping it in a special lagging jacket which can be bought cheaply from DIY outlets. Check that it bears the British Standard Kitemark (BS 5615). Fitting it is an easy job and the insulation will pay for itself within a matter of weeks.

Insulate the loft with glass or mineral fibre blanket or loose fill granules. Provided access to the space is reasonably good, you can easily do the job yourself; if it is difficult you would do better to employ a professional firm to use machinery to blow the insulation into position. When doing it yourself, wear safety goggles to stop dust getting in your eyes and a face mask to protect your nose and mouth. Do not insulate under the cold water tank as the heat which comes up from below stops it freezing. Don't block the eaves or there will be no ventilation so condensation and rot will develop. Do insulate the trap to the loft; enclose it in plastic so the insulation doesn't fall off when the trap is raised. Loft insulation should pay for itself within one to five years, depending on the area involved.

Insulate cylinders and pipes by wrapping the cold water storage tank either in leftover wrapping from the loft floor or glass or mineral fibre blanket. Alternatively cut polystyrene slabs to size and fit them round it. Never insulate below it (see above). Both hot and cold water pipes should be lagged to prevent heat loss and freezing. Either bandage strips of glass or mineral fibre round the pipe in overlapping layers or use preformed or moulded pipe insulation which is fastened with tape. Lag taps and valves separately in case you need to get to them quickly.

Insulate ceilings if, for some reason, you cannot insulate the loft floor. Stick up polystyrene tiles or boards made of special insulating material. With the tiles, always buy a self-extinguishing type and don't put them up near cookers or boilers as even these burn more readily than other building materials. Don't paint polystyrene with gloss paint which acts as a solvent and dissolves it; use fire resistant emulsion.

Insulate the floor, especially if you are not putting down fitted carpets which, to some degree, act as insulation. Either lift the floorboards and put insulation blanket between the joists or fit thermal underlay. Hardboard panels, covered with carpet paper, underlay and, finally carpet or other flooring, will do a good job fairly cheaply.

Insulate doors and windows with proprietary products from DIY shops. Most types are effective but you may need to pay more to find one that is aesthetically pleasing. Put a flap over the inside of the letterbox and hang thick, lined curtains at large windows. Take care when draught-proofing not to remove all sources of air as this leads to condensation, to people feeling drowsy and to heaters not working efficiently.

Insulate solid and cavity walls. Solid walls can be insulated from the outside by bonding a layer of insulating material on to the wall and covering it with protective coating. This method is not cheap. To insulate the inside of solid walls you must line them with insulating material. Cavity walls can have the space filled with either bonded expanded polystyrene beads, mineral fibre or foam. This needs to be done by a professional firm and should pay for itself within four to ten years.

Double glazing may be of the sealed unit or secondary sash type. Sealed units consist of two panes of glass which are sealed together at the factory. They can be fitted into existing window frames, if suitable, or as replacement windows. Secondary sashes are fitted in addition to existing windows. Frames for both types may be wood, metal or plastic. You can fit double glazing yourself using one of the many kits on the market which vary in degrees of sophistication. If you are having double glazing fitted professionally choose a firm which is a member of the *Glass and Glazing Federation* (6 Mount Row, London W1Y 6DY) who operate a scheme which protects you if your contractor goes out of business. Members work to a code of ethics and their staff should carry a GGF identity card.

Use the remaining space on this page to make notes about the type of insulation you have installed, its cost and – where appropriate – guarantee period. With materials you fit yourself, make a note of where they are purchased.

Making Your Home Secure

The increase in domestic burglary is alarming and it makes sense to render it as difficult as possible for thieves to break into your home. The first step is to talk to your Crime Prevention Officer who works at the police station and who will, for no charge, visit your home and advise you on what security measures to take. You can also consult the company which handles your household contents insurance or the *British Insurance Association, Aldermary House, Queen Street, London EC4N 1TU.*

LOCKS AND ALARMS

You can fit suitable locks to doors and windows but it is essential to use them. Even if you leave the house for a very short period of time, lock up.

Different types of window (e.g., sash, casement) need different types of window lock. Your CPO will advise on the best type for your home and you will find that most hardware shops sell a selection and can tell you which type fits your kind of window. Some locks are designed to allow you to open the window a short distance while still keeping it locked against intruders.

Discuss with the CPO whether you should fit a burglar alarm and if so, what type. Simple alarms are a DIY job to fix but more sophisticated devices need professional installation.

Mark your possessions indelibly so that if they are stolen the police will have an easier job in tracing them. The police can advise on this. Simple etching kits can be used to engrave your postcode and the first two letters of your name on things like cameras, televisions, video cassette recorders, radios, computers and hi-fi equipment. Ultra violet pens can be used to record the same information on things like pictures and ornaments which you don't want to mark. The information shows up under ultra-violet lamps (all police stations have one).

If you own valuable jewellery and do not wish to keep it in the bank consider fitting a safe somewhere in your home. Safes are usually fireproof and are therefore also good places in which to store important documents.

Don't make it easy for burglars to get into your home by leaving things like ladders lying around. Paint drainpipes with anti-climb paint which remains sticky and slippery all the time. Fix exterior lights to your home and switch them on at night. Try to make people think there is someone in the home even when there isn't. Time switches can be used to turn lamps and radios on and off and you can fit a special switch which turns lights on when it gets dark – whatever time of day that is. In urban and densely populated areas get together with neighbours to form a Neighbourhood Watch Scheme. These have been established in many places and have reduced the crime rate.

NOTES

Making Your Home Secure

Use this space to record what locks you have fitted to doors and windows, the telephone number of the neighbour authorized to switch off your burglar alarm and any other security data you wish to log. Do not write anything which might be useful to burglars getting hold of this book.

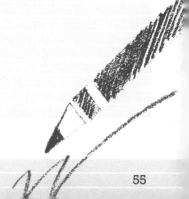

Coping With Fire

Fire moves fast and you must too if it breaks out in your home. Whatever your fire-fighting equipment, the most important thing is to get everyone out of the place as quickly as possible and then call the fire brigade.

FIRE BRIGADE (TEL. NO. 999)

Non-emergency fire brigade tel. no.

Close the door of the room in which fire has broken out and, if possible, place a rug or blanket along the bottom of the door. This cuts off the oxygen supply which feeds the flames and hopefully will help contain the fire.

FIRE FIGHTING

You may want to tackle small isolated fires yourself. If a fire is caused by electrical equipment do not use water to put it out until you have switched off at the socket outlet or the mains. Fires involving fats or oils (except oil heaters) should never be extinguished with water; use a damp cloth, large plate or fire blanket. If an oil heater catches fire use water directly on the heater to cool it down before attempting to extinguish the surrounding flames. Stand well clear so you are not burnt in case the fire flares up as you throw buckets of water on to it.

Only tackle small fires, otherwise evacuate the premises fast.

Fire practice isn't just something done in offices and schools. Everyone in your home should know what the safe escape routes are and have been along them if they involve things like jumping from balconies or climbing out of windows. When you lock outside doors at night be sure that the keys are left reasonably near them so that people can get out in case of fire. Stout bolts may be a better bet than locks.

PREVENTING FIRE

▶ Be aware constantly of the danger of fire and take precautions against it.
▶ Always put a guard round an open fire when you leave a room.
▶ Don't leave tea towels or washing draped over or near a cooker or heater.
▶ Take care not to put portable heaters near curtains or upholstery.
▶ Never leave chip pans unattended on a hob and ensure that electric flexes don't trail over it.
▶ Do not overload power points, and use the correct wattage light bulb in fittings to avoid burning lampshades.
▶ Do not run electric flexes under rugs or carpets.
▶ Keep a firm eye on smokers in the household. Never leave smouldering cigarettes in ashtrays or tip them into a waste bin. Check all rooms before you go to bed and discourage anyone who smokes in bed.

Fire Fighting Appliances

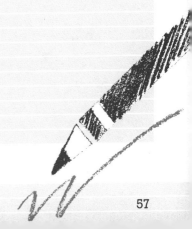

Fire extinguishers should conform to BS 5423 and have FOC (Fire Offices Committee) and FETA approval. They use different constituents – water, foam, Halon and dry powder. The best buy is a multi-purpose extinguisher and it is sensible to take advice on what you need from the local fire brigade or *FETA (Fire Extinguisher Trade Association*, 48A Eden St, Kingston on Thames, Surrey KT1 1EE).

A fire blanket is useful for extinguishing kitchen fires and should be fixed close to the cooker or hob ready for use when needed. A smoke detector (more than one if your home is large) will give warning of fire by emitting a blast of sound when smoke reaches a certain level. Follow the manufacturer's instructions about where to site one and how to check it.

List here details of fire extinguishers, blankets and smoke detectors. Note the date on which they need maintenance or (with smoke detectors) the last date when you fitted new batteries. Items to log include fire extinguishers (include car fire extinguisher), fire blankets and smoke detectors. Make a note of the fire extinguisher brand, what you paid for it and where you bought it.

FIRE FIGHTING EQUIPMENT

Telephones

The number of telephones you need and where you site them will depend on the size of your home and whether you use the telephones for business, private calls or both. Your quarterly rental charge will depend on the number of telephones you have and you pay in addition for calls you make, at different charges depending on the time of day when you make them and the distance involved. If you do not pay your telephone bill within a short period of receiving it the telephone company will cut you off and you will have to pay a charge to be reconnected. You can either pay the bill by cheque or cash or buy telephone stamps from your local Post Office and stick these on a card to put towards the total. When it comes to choosing the actual handset there is a wide variety of designs and colours with a selection of special features. Telephones which are sold marked with a green circle have been tested and approved for use on the British Telecom telephone system. Those bearing a red triangle are not approved and if you connect one your service may be withdrawn by BT.

SPECIAL FEATURES

Think about which of these features you need when making your choice. **Last number redial** automatically dials the last number you tried.

Volume control usually on the bell or tone caller but on some models you can turn up your caller's voice if you can't hear it clearly.

Memory can store up to 10 numbers you regularly dial. You get them by pushing a memory/recall button and just one of the digits which relates to the number stored.

Cut-out button prevents outgoing calls being made.

Mute, silence, confidentiality button silences the sound from your end of the line.

Hands-free calling facility enables you to put the handset down and talk to a microphone in the base. Models with on-hook dialling enable you to dial without lifting the handset.

Call timer indicates how long your last call lasted.

Cordless telephones enable you to carry the handset around with you while answering the door, gardening and even for a short distance away from home. They work on a radio frequency which connects handset and the base which needs to be plugged into the ring mains. The handset needs to be recharged by placing on the base overnight. Cordless telephone sets vary from basic models to more sophisticated ones with buzzers and the ability for the person with the handset to talk to a person using the base. Cordless telephone handsets will not work if they get wet.

A car telephone is useful if you spend a lot of time travelling and need to maintain contact with business colleagues or family.

Telephone Bill Record

Date	Amount	Total local / long distance	Notes	Date paid

Use these pages to monitor your telephone bill costs. In the notes section write down any information which would account for especially high or low bills (e.g., mother ill, we were on holiday etc.). Also, be sure to include the dates of alarm calls booked through the operator, and so on.

Telephone Bill Record

Date	Amount	Total local / long distance	Notes	Date paid

Date	Amount	Total local / long distance	Notes	Date paid

Simple Plumbing Repairs

For serious problems with home waterworks you need to be able to call on the services of a qualified plumber. From time to time, you may also need a 24-hour emergency service if you have a burst pipe or flood in the middle of the night and your usual plumber cannot come out. But simple plumbing repairs can be done easily by amateurs and doing these yourself will save you a lot of money.

UNBLOCKING A SINK

Small blockages can usually be cleared by an application of proprietary drainer or a handful of washing soda dissolved in 0.5 litre (1 pint) of hot water. Otherwise, block off the overflow and use a sink plunger. For blockages that can't be shifted by these methods you need to remove the bottom of the U bend (put a bucket underneath) and wiggle a piece of flexible wire down the sink.

RADIATOR AIRLOCKS

You will need the 'key' which should come with the system. Use it to open the vent valve at one end of the radiator, holding a container below it to catch any water when it flows. Initially, there will be a hissing sound; after that water flows and you can tighten the valve again.

FROZEN PIPES

Avoid these where possible by putting plugs in baths, sinks and basins when the temperature starts to drop to prevent the outlets freezing. If your taps drip persistently, put salt in the waste traps to help stop them freezing up. When pipes are frozen take a hair dryer and play it along the frozen area. If this does not work, call a plumber. When the pipes have thawed out, check the joints on copper piping as freezing can push them out of their compression fittings.

PIPE AIRLOCKS

If when you turn on a tap only a feeble trickle comes out you probably have an airlock in the pipes. You usually hear a knocking sound. You can fix this yourself if you have hot and cold taps in the kitchen but if there is a mixer tap you will need a plumber to cope. Take a piece of hosepipe and two adjustable clips and fit the hose on to the hot and cold taps in a U shape. Tighten the clips well with a screwdriver. Turn on first the hot and then the cold tap. Leave both running for a few minutes so that the mains pressure from the cold tap forces the water and air back through the pipes into the hot water storage tank or cylinder. If this does not clear the airlock, after five minutes, leave if for quarter of an hour and then try again. If this still does not work, call a plumber.

Plumbing Notes

Use this page to keep a note of any plumbing repairs carried out and how much they cost. Don't forget to include DIY repairs as well as professional ones. Head the page with clear directions on the location of the main stopcock, which direction it turns in and any problems associated with it such as stiffness or difficulty of reach.

STOPCOCK NOTES Type of repair	Cost	Date	Notes

Paying the Rates

The rates on your home are a tax levied by your local authority and designed to pay for local services such as education, refuse collection, social services and so on. The local authority is required by law to provide these services and you cannot refuse to pay them even if, for example, you have no children and therefore do not require educational facilities. Rates are levied on both domestic and business properties and are payable by the person who has control of the property; this is usually the occupier, whether owner or tenant, but not a lodger.

If you have a low income or (for reasons explained below) an exceptionally high rateable value on your home, you may be eligible for a rate rebate. If you think you fall into this category enquire at your town hall.

HOW RATES ARE ASSESSED

The amount of money you pay in rates is based on two factors: the rateable value of your home (see below) and the rate in the £ which the council agrees to levy. The rateable value of your home is decided by a valuation officer. You are required to fill in a form which gives details of your property, the number of rooms, amenities and so forth and the calculation is based on this. The general state of repair does not affect your rateable value but genuine home improvement like the building of an extension, or the addition of a garden shed or garage will increase

it. From time to time the valuation officer will visit your home to check that the information you have supplied is correct and to notice any improvements which you may have failed to tell the local authority about. If you believe your home is over-valued you can apply to have your rateable value decreased. You might discover that your neighbour pays less rates than you or long-term building work might start nearby on a motorway. Any decrease in the amenities around your home – such as the loss of tennis courts in your local park – might well prove grounds for a decrease of rateable value.

Rate bills are payable half yearly, usually in April and October. Most local authorities also allow you to pay them in ten monthly instalments throughout the year. To find out what arrangements your local authority operates, write to them at the address given on the rates demand note.

Keep a regular note of the amount of rates you're paying and use this record to keep a check on the sums you pay and to make sure the bills are paid at the correct time.

Year	Rate levied	Date paid	Amount paid

RATEABLE VALUE OF PROPERTY: £

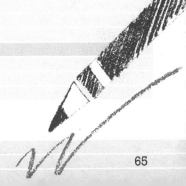

External Maintenance and Repairs

New or old, your home will need to be kept in good repair if it is to function properly and to maintain its value. Some external repairs are DIY jobs (e.g., cleaning gutters, keeping paths free of lichen and weeds) while others – unless you are expert – are best left to professionals (e.g., hanging roof tiles, thatching).

Try to do external repairs when the weather is good so that the work itself is less hazardous and the risks of newly laid concrete freezing or ladders slipping is reduced. Because external work can be dangerous take care to avoid risks. Hire or borrow a good ladder if you don't own one and get the proper equipment if you need to do a job like repointing the top of a high wall or painting the outside of top floor windows. The following list suggests areas that you should check each year. Most of the time remedial work can be kept to a minimum provided it is done regularly and before serious deterioration sets in. However, major work will be necessary from time to time and it is sensible to allow for this when planning your annual budget.

Roofs, tiles, thatch, chimneystacks, flashings
Gutters and drainpipes
Windows and windowsills
Brickwork and plaster/rendering
Damp proof course
External doors and locks
Patios, paths, steps
Overhanging trees, hedges
Walls and fences
Garage, shed, outhouses

If you share facilities like a wall or fence with a neighbour the deeds to your home will state who is the actual owner and who therefore is responsible for maintenance and repairs. It is difficult to get your neighbour to do these you can either have recourse to the law (which could make for bad feelings) or contribute to the repairs yourself. It really is important to keep the area surrounding your property looking good, especially if you want to sell. A decrepit exterior also makes it easier for thieves to break in.

MATT EMULSION

External Maintenance and Repair

Roofs: tiles, thatch, chimneystacks, flashings

Gutters and drainpipes

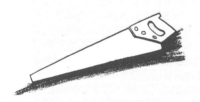

Make Spring the time you check the exterior of your home so that any work can be carried out while the weather is good and there is less risk of newly laid concrete freezing or ladders slipping. Here is a checklist of points to consider. Use the remaining space to make a note of work that you need doing/ has been done and how much it costs.

Windows and windowsills	Brickwork and plaster/rendering

External Maintenance and Repairs

Damp proof course	External doors and locks	Patios, paths, steps

Overhanging trees,
hedges

Walls and fences

Garage, shed, outhouse

Home Decorating Record

Keeping a home decorating record is useful for several reasons. It tells you exactly what you used when doing up the room and how much you needed of things like paint and wallcoverings. If you have to match up fabric or flooring at a later date you will have all the details to hand and when it comes to redecorating you can order the amounts required without having to go through the tedious procedure of measuring again and calculating quantities all over again.

On the following pages you can log information on what was used when decorating each room. It's worth making the effort to write down as much detail as possible. You might, for example, be able to obtain the last bit of matching fabric in the land if you can supply the manufacturer with its name, reference number and colourway correctly.

Be sure to make a note of points which could vary when you come to redecorate. The amount of wallcovering and fabric needed will depend on the length of 'drop' on the pattern and you should note this along with the other details. This saves time, and money, in the long run. Don't forget to make a note of any special items which are specifically intended to enhance the effect of the room's decor. Light fittings, lampshades, cushions and so on may be listed in the room-by-room inventory (see pages 4 to 33), but it's a good idea to log stockists in this section in case you want to replace something or buy extra. The final page for each room is intended for you to stick down sample swatches of wallpaper, fabric, etc. Armed with these samples you can take your log book shopping and be sure that what you buy will match with what you already have. Don't stick in a flooring sample as it will make the logbook too bulky. Cut out a picture of it from the manufacturer's literature and use that instead.

Living Room

PAINT	QUANTITY	NOTES

WALLCOVERING	QUANTITY	NOTES

Living Room

FLOOR COVERING	QUANTITY	NOTES

FABRIC (BLIND)	QUANTITY	NOTES

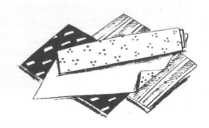

Living Room

FABRIC (OTHER)	QUANTITY	NOTES

MISCELLANEOUS	QUANTITY	NOTES

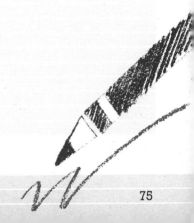

Dining Room

PAINT	QUANTITY	NOTES

WALLCOVERING	QUANTITY	NOTES

Dining Room

FLOOR COVERING	QUANTITY	NOTES

FABRIC (BLIND)	QUANTITY	NOTES

Dining Room

FABRIC (OTHER)	QUANTITY	NOTES

MISCELLANEOUS	QUANTITY	NOTES

Kitchen

PAINT	QUANTITY	NOTES

WALLCOVERING	QUANTITY	NOTES

Kitchen

FLOOR COVERING	QUANTITY	NOTES

FABRIC (BLIND)	QUANTITY	NOTES

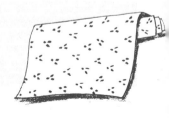

Kitchen

FABRIC (OTHER)	QUANTITY	NOTES

MISCELLANEOUS	QUANTITY	NOTES

Bedroom 1

PAINT	QUANTITY	NOTES

WALLCOVERING	QUANTITY	NOTES

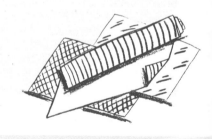

Bedroom 1

FLOOR COVERING	QUANTITY	NOTES

FABRIC (BLIND)	QUANTITY	NOTES

Bedroom 1

FABRIC (OTHER)	QUANTITY	NOTES

MISCELLANEOUS	QUANTITY	NOTES

Bedroom 2

PAINT	QUANTITY	NOTES

WALLCOVERING	QUANTITY	NOTES

Bedroom 2

FLOOR COVERING	QUANTITY	NOTES

FABRIC (BLIND)	QUANTITY	NOTES

Bedroom 2

FABRIC (OTHER)	QUANTITY	NOTES

MISCELLANEOUS	QUANTITY	NOTES

Bedroom 3

PAINT	QUANTITY	NOTES

WALLCOVERING	QUANTITY	NOTES

FLOOR COVERING	QUANTITY	NOTES

Bedroom 3

FABRIC (BLIND)	QUANTITY	NOTES

FABRIC (OTHER)	QUANTITY	NOTES

MISCELLANEOUS	QUANTITY	NOTES

Bathroom

PAINT	QUANTITY	NOTES

WALLCOVERING	QUANTITY	NOTES

FLOOR COVERING	QUANTITY	NOTES

Bathroom

FABRIC (BLIND)	QUANTITY	NOTES

FABRIC (OTHER)	QUANTITY	NOTES

MISCELLANEOUS	QUANTITY	NOTES

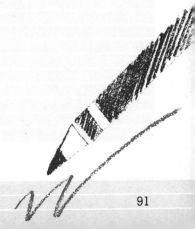

Playroom / Study

PAINT	QUANTITY	NOTES

WALLCOVERING	QUANTITY	NOTES

FLOOR COVERING	QUANTITY	NOTES

Playroom/Study

FABRIC (BLIND)	QUANTITY	NOTES

FABRIC (OTHER)	QUANTITY	NOTES

MISCELLANEOUS	QUANTITY	NOTES

Other Rooms / Outbuildings

PAINT	QUANTITY	NOTES

WALLCOVERING	QUANTITY	NOTES

FLOOR COVERING	QUANTITY	NOTES

FABRIC (BLIND)	QUANTITY	NOTES

FABRIC (OTHER)	QUANTITY	NOTES

MISCELLANEOUS	QUANTITY	NOTES

Insurance Policies

As well as providing the roof over your head, your home is a major asset so it is essential that it should be insured against all forms of loss or damage. An insurance broker or your bank will advise on what policy is most suitable and you must be sure to keep up with inflation when working out the value of the items insured. You need a policy for the building(s), household contents – making sure that those which leave the home with you (such as umbrellas and diamond earrings) are covered for this – and, possibly, insurance to cover people who work in your home or to cover damage that your pets may inflict on other people or their homes. On this page list your policies, stating type, policy number, date when the premium is due and the premium paid. You may also wish to list other policies such as life insurance, medical insurance and holiday insurance as well.

TYPE OF POLICY

POLICY NO.	PREMIUM DUE ON	AMOUNT PAID

Insurance Policies

PREMIUM DUE ON	AMOUNT PAID

Using Local Transport

Trains – day/night	Bus – day/night	Tube – day/night

Use these pages to make notes about local transport, where to get hold of it and what hours it operates. You may like to note down times of first and last bus or train.

Local railway station tel. no.

Local bus or coach station tel. no.

Taxi firms tel. no.

Mini-cab firms tel. no.

Local underground station tel. no.

Local car hire firm tel. no.

Schools and Children's Activities

SCHOOL (NAME AND ADDRESS)	TEL. NO.	OFFICE HOURS	EMERGENCY TEL. NO.

SCHOOL RUNS		
Name	Tel. No.	Times when never available

Organizing the family's education and leisure can be complex. Write down all the details you can think of on these pages so that anyone suddenly co-opted on to the school run can see at a glance what to do. Make a note of the names of the head teacher and the class teacher.

SCHOOL RUN TIMETABLE	a.m. (name)	p.m. (name)
Monday		
Tuesday		
Wednesday		
Thursday		
Friday		
Saturday		

NAMES OF CHILDREN ON RUN	ADDRESSES

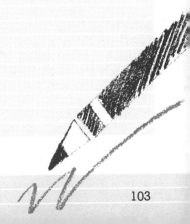

Schools and Children's Activities

DINNER MONEY

Amount payable	Cheque made out to	Day due

SCHOOL UNIFORM SUPPLIER(S)

SECONDHAND SCHOOL UNIFORM SUPPLIER(S)

LEISURE ACTIVITIES (BALLET, BROWNIES, SCOUTS, SWIMMING OR COMPUTER CLUB, ETC.)

Activity	day of week	time	contact tel. no.	driver to/from

Specialist Shops and Services

NAME, ADDRESS, TEL. NO.	GOODS/SERVICE OFFERED

Use these pages for listing any specialist shops or services you have or might in the future find useful (including mail order). Clip out any advertisements or articles from newspapers and magazines of organizations you might want to use and stick them in here.

Car Log

Cars generate a fair amount of paperwork so it's wise to keep a separate file in which to store it and ensure that vital documents don't get lost. Use these pages to list details that you might need in a hurry (ignition key number, tyre pressures) and to jog your memory about things like the date when the insurance premium or road tax fall due. If you have more than one car, divide this page in half and list details of both and reserve separate servicing records for each.

MAKE OF CAR

Model

Year

Registration number *(etch this on the windows with a special kit so that the car becomes an unattractive proposition to casual thieves; windows are expensive and fiddly to replace)*

Colour

Touch-up paint shade

Engine number

Chassis number

Ignition key number

Petrol cap key number

Radio/tape player details

Road tax due on

MOT test due on

Insurance policy number

Insurance policy premium due on

People covered to drive car

Driving licence(s) no(s).

Motoring organization(s) joined

Membership number and coverage

Subscription renewal date

Emergency breakdown number

Tyre pressures

Front wheels

Back wheels

Car Log

SERVICING/REPAIR RECORD

Date

Work done

New parts fitted

Garage used

Cost

Builders' Estimates and Quotations

Estimates and quotations are both advance indications of what you will have to pay someone to carry out a specified piece of work for you. The two words don't have precise legal definitions but, in general, it is true to say that an *estimate* is a rough idea of what the work will cost and a *quotation* is a statement of what it will cost. Estimates are usually given verbally; you might ring round two or three plumbers to enquire roughly how much it would cost to fit a shower cubicle in the spare bedroom and they could give you an approximate figure over the telephone. When a quotation is required, the workman in question will need to visit your home and see how much material will be required and whether there are likely to be any problems with running pipes to the new site and installing the shower.

If you get an estimate and decide to accept it you may well find that the work costs more because of some unforeseen snag or the fact that the materials cost more than anticipated. With a quotation both you and the workman should be clear in your minds what is being quoted for. He can then supply you with a written quotation which should specify the materials to be used and give some detail of the work and making good which will be done. Once you have accepted a quotation in writing there is a contract between you and the workman and the work must be done for that price. Only if *you* change your mind about something, has he the right to alter it.

COMPARING QUOTATIONS

With major pieces of work it is a good idea to get two or three quotations from different firms. If they vary considerably, try and find out what the reason is. It may be that one firm is short of work and keen to do the job so tenders cheaply or it may be that the lowest quotation is because the materials used will be poor quality. It is important to find this out as having a 'cowboy' job done may mean that you have problems with the work afterwards (leaks, badly finished work) or that you have to pay someone else to patch it up at a later date.

For work like home extensions, double glazing and fencing it is a good idea to ask your preferred contractor if you can look at a previous job. When doing so, take the opportunity to ask the householders whether there were any problems with the firm which did the work.

If time is of the essence on a particular piece of work, make this clear when you accept the quotation and ask the workman to confirm in writing that the work will be started by a particular date and finished by another. Keep copies of the original quotation and of any other correspondence you have with the contractor as you may need them as evidence if anything goes wrong with the job.

Use this space for notes about estimates and quotations you have requested so that you can make comparisons before deciding.

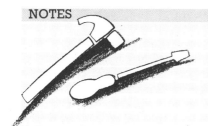

NOTES

113

Removing Marks from Furniture

Whether antique or modern, furniture is expensive to buy, so it makes sense to keep it in good condition. If it is very valuable you should have dents and marks removed professionally. Otherwise use the following treatments.

Alcohol stains on wood Can usually be removed by thorough polishing; otherwise rub along the grain of the wood with metal polish or a paste made from linseed oil and cigarette ash.

Bruises on wood Soak a piece of blotting paper in water and fold it to form a thick wad. Place over the bruise and hold a hot iron over the blotting paper taking care that no part of the soleplate touches the wood. Polish as usual.

Burns on wood Rub along the grain with metal polish except on waxed or oil-finished wood which should be rubbed with turpentine. With deep burns, first scrape out the burned wood until the hole is clean then fill it with a matching wood filler (from hardware and DIY shops). Use small amounts of shoe polish if you need to tint the filler to produce an exact match. Smooth the filler until it is level with the rest of the surface and when dry polish on the surface as you usually do.

Dents in wood With solid wood, first put a little warm water in the dent to see if it will swell the fibres and eradicate it. If this doesn't work, clean the wax off the damaged area, place a wad of wet blotting paper over the dent and apply a warm iron, taking care that it does not touch the wood. When dry, use a suitable shade of shoe polish to tone the raised wood to the colour of the rest. Polish as usual. In veneered wood, dents split the surface. Buy a small piece of similar veneer (art shops are a good place to look), lay it over the damaged area and cut an oval shape through both layers of veneer, round the dent. Remove the damaged section with a wood chisel. Dampen the new patch to make it pliable and fix into position with wood adhesive, taking care to wipe off any surplus before it marks the rest of the surface. Place a weight over the patch to keep it flat while the adhesive dries. When dry, smooth over with fine abrasive paper, tint with shoe polish, if necessary, and polish as usual.

Heat marks on wood Rub with turpentine along the grain.

Ink marks on wood Dab with household bleach applied on a cotton wool bud and blot immediately with kitchen paper. You may need to do this several times, but act quickly so that drastic bleaching does not occur. For large spills, use a special wood bleach following the manufacturer's instructions.

Scratches on wood Either use a proprietary scratch dressing or rub over the scratch with a wax crayon of the right colour.

Water marks on wood Rub along the grain with turpentine and if this does not work repeat the process using a metal polish.

CARING FOR CARPETS

Carpets are another expensive item and need care to keep them in good condition. Vacuum them regularly but shampoo as infrequently as possible. You can either employ a professional firm or do it yourself either with a manual applicator (which is tiring) or with a hired steam cleaner, which does a very effective job. When shampooing a carpet yourself, by whatever method, take care not to overwet it or colour from the backing may seep through and discolour the pile. Overwetted backing may also shrink or become distorted. Place pieces of kitchen foil under the legs of furniture to protect the carpet until it is completely dry.

Beer on carpets Can be flushed out with a squirt from a soda syphon or by sponging with warm, clear water then blotting well with a clean white cloth or kitchen paper. Apply carpet shampoo to remaining marks.

Blood on carpets Squirt with a soda syphon or sponge with cold water and blot dry. Apply made-up carpet shampoo.

Candle wax on carpets Gently scrape off as much of the deposit as possible with a spoon. Place blotting paper over the mark and apply the tip of a warm iron to melt the wax and allow it to be absorbed into the blotting paper. Remove remaining marks by dabbing with methylated spirit.

Chewing gum on carpets Buy a proprietary aerosol remover which will freeze the deposit so you can break it up and brush it away. Otherwise, hold a plastic bag of ice cubes on the gum to freeze it.

Coffee on carpets Flush with a soda syphon or sponge with warm water and blot dry. Apply made-up carpet shampoo to remaining marks.

Fat on carpets Scrape up as much as possible then apply a stain remover followed by a carpet shampoo.

Ketchup and bottled sauces on carpets Scoop up as much as possible and wipe off the rest with a clean, damp cloth, taking care not to spread the stain. If the marks are dried, apply a solution of equal parts of glycerine and water and leave it on for an hour before wiping off and rubbing in the lather from made-up carpet shampoo. Wipe in the direction of the pile with a cloth wrung out in warm water.

Lipstick on carpets Use a blunt knife to scrape off as much deposit as possible, then apply a stain remover or paint brush cleaner. Finally, remove any indelible lipstick marks with methylated spirit.

Milk on carpets Must be cleared as quickly as possible since once it dries the smell is impossible to eradicate. Flush with a soda syphon or warm water, blot thoroughly and apply carpet shampoo. Treat remaining marks with stain remover.

Vomit on carpets Remove the deposit and flush the area with a squirt from a soda syphon, then blot with a clean white cloth. Rub in the lather from made-up carpet shampoo and repeat applications until the mark disappears. Finally, rinse with warm water, to which you have added a few drops of antiseptic, and blot.

Shoppers' Rights

When you buy goods in a shop you enter into a contract with the seller. All you need to do is to pay the price asked and take the goods home or have them delivered. The seller has certain responsibilities to you in connection with the goods and if they are not met, then you are entitled to either a replacement or to have your money back.

The first point is that the goods must match their description. This means that what you buy must be as described on the packaging in terms of size, finish, number of pieces in the box and so on. If, for example, you buy a 20-piece set of china and find that there are only 19 pieces or that they are in a different pattern or colour to the one you selected which is shown on the box, the seller is in breach of the Sale of Goods Act. He is also in breach if when selling he has told you things which are not true, e.g., that a silk shirt is machine washable when it is not. Similarly if *you* ask the seller for an item with particular qualities and the goods do not have them he is also in breach of his responsibilities, as for example, if you ask for a wood adhesive to stick a leg on a chair and are supplied with one for model making.

Goods you buy also have to be of 'merchantable quality', i.e., of a reasonable standard. This means that they must not be damaged unless your attention is drawn to the damage before you buy them. They must also work properly and continue to do so for a reasonable period of time. The law does not lay down how long goods should last but you can make assumptions about this depending on what the item is. You would not expect something like a lipstick case to last as long as a refrigerator. Sale goods must also be of merchantable quality unless they are described as 'imperfect' or 'substandard'. It is the buyer's responsibility to find out what the defects are.

BUYING SECONDHAND GOODS

These must also be of merchantable quality if bought from a shop but not if bought privately, perhaps through a small ad in a local paper. You cannot expect secondhand goods to be in the same condition as new but they should be in reasonable condition and functioning properly, depending on how old they are and how much you pay for them. If defects are pointed out at the time of sale you will not have a case against the trader if you find the defects render the purchase unusable.

Goods you buy in addition have to be fit for their purpose. This means they must do what they claim to do. A sweater should have two sleeves, a teapot should pour and a washing machine should wash. If you want an item for a particular purpose and ask the seller for it specifically you will have a case if what is supplied is not suitable. The fitness for purpose specification also applies to secondhand goods although, like merchantable quality, not to goods sold by private individuals.

Buying by Post

You have the rare advantage when shopping by post of being able to decide you don't like something – without any particular reason – and sending it back. You cannot do this when buying goods over the counter in a shop unless there is something wrong with the product (see page 118). Postal shopping also offers the advantages of saving travelling time and transport costs; postage is often cheaper than making a journey by train or bus or than using your car and paying for petrol and parking.

Your legal rights are exactly the same as when buying goods from shops and if there are any problems with an item you can obtain a replacement or refund.

KEEP NOTES

When ordering goods by mail order keep a note of what you have ordered, the amount paid and how (cheque/postal order no.), and of when you post the order. Most mail order companies claim to despatch their goods within 28 days. If you need something sooner than this – perhaps something to wear for a special occasion – write 'Delivery by .... time is of the essence of the contract' on the order form and sign it. If the goods do not reach you in time, you are then legally entitled to ask for a full refund. Do not expect miracles though; companies need time to pack goods and process them through their system and the Post Office needs time to deliver them.

CONSUMER PROTECTION

Many large mail order businesses and those who produce the big general catalogues subscribe to the Mail Order Traders' Association and have agreed to abide by a code of practice. If you wish to complain about a member write to the *Association* at 507 Corn Exchange Building, Fenwick Street, Liverpool.

Goods ordered through the advertisement pages of newspapers and magazines are covered by a code of practice operated by the Mail Order Publishers' Association. This states that any advertisement for goods in such a publication must make the main terms of the offer quite clear and supply information about quantity, quality, price and conditions of sale. They must state clearly whether the price includes postage and packaging and, if not, how much these will be. Claims for 'free approval' must not be made if the prospective buyer has to pay return postage on unwanted goods. Despatch dates should always be given where payment is requested in advance.

COMPLAINTS

If you need to complain about advertisements in publications or goods bought via them, write, in the first instance, to the Advertisement Director of the newspaper or magazine in which you saw it. *The Mail Order Publishers' Association* is at 1 New Burlington Street, London W1.

Complaining About Faulty Goods

Most people have to complain about faulty goods at some time and it is important to follow the right procedure. The first thing is to be sure that you have a genuine complaint. You must know what you are complaining about in terms of the item and also be quite sure that it is not your fault because of using something for a purpose for which it is not intended or failing to follow instructions. Know too what sort of redress you want – is it a refund, a replacement item or a credit note? Where cases are proven shops like to give a credit note because it means that the money will at least be spent for the second time in their store. But you do not have to accept a credit note – and bear in mind that it does tie you down to shopping in the same place – unless you want it. Once a shopkeeper has agreed that your complaint is justified, you are entitled to receive your money back in full.

PROCEDURE FOR COMPLAINTS

Here are the correct steps to follow when making a complaint. Go back to the shop or supplier where you purchased the goods (product or service) as soon as possible. Don't make your complaint to whoever is serving behind the counter as they are unlikely to have the authority to deal with it. Ask to see the buyer or manager. Where possible, take the faulty goods with you and also the receipt. Do not hand either over as they are evidence to support your case. You will need them if you eventually have to go to court. Decide whether what the seller offers you is worth accepting. A partial refund or credit note may be worth taking if the amount of money involved is small and you lack time to take your complaint further.

If the seller refuses to accept your complaint, go home and write a letter to him, spelling out in detail what you require and send a copy to the firm's head office (where appropriate). The letter should include all the factual details of your complaint but avoid making angry or irrelevant statements. Keep a copy of this and any other correspondence about the complaint in case you eventually have to go to court.

If you are still getting nowhere, ask your local Citizens' Advice Bureau or Consumer Advice Centre whether it is worth taking your complaint further. In some instances, the seller may be a member of a trade association which operates a Code of Practice which includes a procedure for dealing with complaints about their members.

If your complaint involves a large amount it may be worth sending the item off for an independent test (not cheap and you pay at this stage) and then taking the matter to court. Ask at your CAB for the name of an appropriate laboratory. Small claims (under £500) can be heard in the Small Claims Court, otherwise you will have to take the case to the County Court.

Guarantees and Service Contracts

Guarantees are not always worth the paper they are written on. In general, it is better to rely on your normal legal rights (see page 118) if you want to complain about faulty goods. In theory, a guarantee is supposed to give you protection over and above these rights but not all do.

Extended guarantees may be offered sometimes; for example, you might buy a refrigerator which carries a five-year guarantee on the compressor. You pay for some extended guarantees at the time of purchase, but do read the small print to check just what you are covered for and also that the scheme is insured. Ask to see the master policy.

Extra long guarantees of up to 20 years are sometimes given on treatments provided by contractors for things such as woodworm or curing damp. Although these sound like a consumer benefit, they may not be if the firm goes out of business during that time or does not permit the guarantee to be passed on if you sell your home. And some extended guarantees are rendered invalid if you fail to apply specified follow-up procedures like replastering with particular materials.

MAKING A CLAIM

Read a guarantee carefully before making a claim under it. Bear in mind that it is not designed to cover fair wear and tear which could lead to breakdown of machinery such as a washing machine; some guarantees do not cover all types of repair or may not pay the full cost of repairs.

Keep all documents relating to a guarantee until its cover period has expired. Make any claims you need to as quickly as possible. If you are without something because it is being repaired under guarantee and the repair takes a long time, try to get the guarantee extended to take account of this.

SERVICE CONTRACTS

Service contracts are designed to keep major pieces of equipment like cookers and central heating boilers going for as long as possible. You pay a sum of money each year which acts as insurance. It usually entitles you to a free service check each year and to free repairs (though parts will need to be paid for) if the machine breaks down.

It is important to understand exactly what a particular service contract does cover. Some offer free labour but you have to pay for parts, others claim that contract holders get priority over other people when it comes to repairs. Read the small print before deciding if you want to pay up.

Service contracts are not cheap and over the years can amount to considerably more than the original price of the machine. With appliances that should be serviced regularly, like central heating boilers, it may be a good idea to have a contract.

Time Saving Tips

▶ Cut down on the time spent bed-making by providing duvets which just need a shake to restore their appearance. Remember that hanging them outdoors over a clothes line or out of a window from time to time will benefit natural fillings.

▶ Keep all your household cleaning products plus things like dusters and polishing cloths in one caddy so that you can move it round the house when cleaning and save endless trips back to base.

▶ Shop as infrequently as you can and save time, temper and transport costs. It could pay you to find some extra cupboard or shelf space so you can buy goods in larger quantities.

▶ Save ironing time by putting clean shirts and blouses on hangers rather than folding them.

▶ Keep the instruction books for all your appliances together in a labelled box file. You will save time hunting around for the particular one you want.

▶ To help defrost a freezer quickly, use a handheld hair dryer or fan heater. Take care, though; remember electricity and water don't mix.

▶ Line the grill pan with kitchen foil and throw the foil away when it gets dirty.

▶ Speed up drying a sweater flat by putting tubes from kitchen paper rolls inside the sleeves. Cover the tubes with kitchen foil or cling film to prevent colour transfer.

▶ Use the soft brush attachment on the vacuum cleaner instead of a cloth duster. It's a much more effective way of cleaning as the dust is sucked into the bag rather than distributed round the house.

▶ Polish furniture only once or twice a year. Otherwise just dust and buff it. More frequent polishing produces a sticky build-up which will eventually need to be removed.

▶ Hang clothes up when you take them off (unless they are to be laundered or dry cleaned) so they don't need any attention like brushing or ironing when you come to wear them again.

▶ Keep a write-and-wipe board in the kitchen and make a note of anything that is running low or has run out. This saves going through the cupboards every time you make a shopping list.

▶ Make your shopping list in the order in which you will buy the items – at different shops or round the supermarket. You are less likely to forget things and have to retrace your steps.

▶ Buy iron-on names for everyone in the house, including adults, and apply them to socks and underwear to speed up sorting out the airing cupboard after they have been washed and dried.

▶ Use an extension lead on the vacuum cleaner to save constantly changing from one socket outlet to another.

Economy Tips

▶ Use a shower instead of a bath. The amount of water and thus electricity is considerably reduced.

▶ Don't preheat a gas or fan-assisted electric oven unless you are cooking something like a soufflé where timing is critical.

▶ Use a pressure cooker to reduce cooking time (especially with pulses) and the amount of fuel used.

▶ Make 'logs' from tightly rolled newspapers (you can buy special machines for this or do it by hand) to supplement wood on open fires and in stoves. Don't use until you have a good fire going.

▶ Stick kitchen foil or special self-adhesive foil on the walls behind radiators so that all the heat they generate is reflected back into the room. Use a sponge-headed dish-mop fixed on to a cane to smooth the foil into place and stick it down with pva adhesive.

▶ If you regularly boil only small amounts of water buy a jug kettle which allows you to boil just enough for one cup of tea or coffee.

▶ Re-use kitchen foil after washing it in a hot detergent solution, brushing gently to remove food particles. Rinse and smooth out.

▶ Put small pieces of cotton wool in the tips of household gloves to prevent your nails making holes in them.

▶ Store soap for a year or so before using it to make it last longer. Keep in a dry warm place like an airing cupboard.

▶ Never use a dishwasher or washing machine until you have a full load (or half load if your washing machine has an appropriate setting).

▶ Buy in bulk when goods are on special offer.

▶ Save the ends of cakes of soap until you have enough to make soap jelly. When you have enough to fill a 600 ml (1 pint) measure cut up the pieces and mix with 600 ml (1 pint) boiling water and 5 ml (1 tsp) laundry borax. Stir until the soap dissolves and pour into bowl and leave until cold. Thereafter use as ordinary soap.

▶ Collect 'money off' coupons from newspapers, magazines and publicity material put through your letter box. Many supermarkets will allow you to use them as payment for any goods, provided that they stock the brand represented. In any case, used carefully, coupons can make definite savings in the household budget.

▶ Old net curtains can be used as excellent cleaning cloths.

▶ Don't throw out faded sheets and curtains. Dyeing them at home can give them a new lease of life at a fraction of the cost of replacement. Follow the instructions on the dye packet to the letter.

▶ Order stair carpet that is about half a metre longer than you need so that every two years you can move (or have it moved) up and down to reduce wear on the edges of the treads.

Cleaning Tips

▸ Aluminium pans tend to discolour with cooking. Remove the stain by boiling up a solution of water to which you have added some acid in the form of lemon juice, apple peelings or vinegar.

▸ Clean windows with a solution of 30 ml (2 tbsp) vinegar to a small bucketful of cold water. Apply with a chamois leather and buff with crumpled newspaper; the printer's ink gives a fine shine.

▸ Light marks on wallpaper can be removed by rubbing with a piece of stale white bread.

▸ Use an old toothbrush to clean behind taps. Dip in bath cleaner and rub well.

▸ Clean a sink by filling with hot water and adding a few drops of household bleach. Wearing household gloves, pull out the plug and replace it upside down. The water then drains away slowly and will thoroughly clean the overflow, plug hole and underside of the plug. Then rinse thoroughly.

▸ Remove black spots on silver by dunking it in a hot, strong salt solution. Rinse, dry and polish as usual.

▸ Clean hairspray off mirrors by wiping with methylated spirit.

▸ Clean a decanter by filling with a warm solution of enzyme detergent and leaving for several hours. Rinse and balance upside down to drain in something stable.

▸ Clean the refrigerator with a solution of 15 ml (1 tbsp) bicarbonate of soda to 1 litre (1¾ pints) warm water. Bicarbonate of soda absorbs smells; using detergent would create them.

▸ Clean a stained teapot by filling it with hot water and 15 ml enzyme detergent and leave for an hour. Rinse well. The spout can be cleaned by packing with salt and leaving for an hour. Use a small bottle brush to remove it all before washing.

▸ Use a brush or vacuum cleaner to keep bamboo furniture dust free. When very dirty scrub it gently with warm soapy water (not synthetic detergent) plus 5 ml (1 tsp) laundry borax added to each 500 ml (1 pint). Rinse with warm salted water 10 ml (2 tsp) to 1 litre (1¾ pints) to help stiffen and bleach it. Wipe dry and allow to dry out naturally, before polishing with furniture cream.

▸ Keep plastic baths clean with a suitable product and remove light scratches by rubbing gently with metal polish.

▸ Badly tarnished brass and copper can be shined up by using salt and lemon juice mixed to a paste and left on for an hour or so.

▸ Descale your kettle according to the manufacturer's instructions. In hard water areas this will need to be done fairly frequently if you use the kettle a lot. Electric kettles should not be allowed to become furred up as this reduces their efficiency and increases running cost.

▸ Clean light bulbs (and increase illumination in your home) by switching off the electricity, removing the bulbs and wiping over gently with a well wrung out damp cloth or a piece of cotton wool dampened with methylated spirit. Never clean bulbs while still in their sockets.

Laundry Tips

► Wash duvets and large blankets in a laundrette machine rather than a domestic one since, when wet, they are very heavy and could disturb the balance of the drum. A commercial tumble dryer is also a more suitable size for drying them. It is important to dry duvets quickly, rather than naturally over a line, as otherwise mildew may develop in the filling.

► Always wash deep dye fabrics separately until no more dye bleeds from them. Check this by including a piece of white fabric in the wash to see how much colour it picks up.

► Never leave damp clothes or linen over a varnished or polished wooden chair or rail as marks may be transferred to the fabric.

► Check all pockets before putting clothes in a washing machine. Paper tissues will disintegrate and leave a film of tiny fibres all over the fabrics and the ink on printed matter like bus tickets will run and cause marking. Coins will probably damage the machine.

► Test for colour fastness before washing any items you are not sure about. Dampen a section like a seam allowance and put it between two pieces of white fabrics (old handkerchiefs are a good idea). Press with the iron set at the temperature for coloured fabric and if any colour comes off on the cotton wash the coloured item separately. Use a solution of cold water detergent or cool suds, rinse in cold water and dry rapidly in a tumble drier or laid flat on an old white towel. Do not hang up or the dye may run and produce a patchy effect.

► Remove stains before washing or the heat of the water may set them irrevocably.

► When washing different fabrics together, set the machine for the temperature and spin programme suitable for the most delicate item. If you regularly put whites into a mixed wash they will eventually develop a greyish tinge and need to be laundered at the correct temperature from time to time.

► Look after your washing machine as well as your washing. Wipe off condensation on the outside and from time to time polish the casing with an aerosol spray. Wash out the detergent dispenser occasionally since if it becomes clogged up insufficient detergent will get through to the washload.

► If coloured items look faded and black garments develop a bloom it is usually because detergent has built up in them. Soak them in a solution of water and half a cup of vinegar to dissolve the soap and restore the colour.

► When washing wool blankets, add a little oil to the final rinse to keep them soft and fluffy.

► Always soak an article completely so that any colour change occurs over all of it. Be sure the washing powder is completely dissolved before putting anything in to soak.

► Iron starched items on the *right* side to increase their resistance to soiling.

► Use a tumble drier with less than its maximum load for more efficient drying.

First Aid in the Home

Accidents occur in even the best-run and most safety-conscious homes. Simple injuries can be treated on the spot (see below), but in general it is as well to know how – and when – you can get hold of professional help quickly. Fill in the following telephone numbers clearly so that you can ring for assistance, and keep your first aid box filled with the items listed.

BASIC FIRST AID KIT

Assorted plasters
Eye pad
Triangular bandage
Safety pins
Scissors with rounded ends
Selection of dressings
Antiseptic cream
Aspirin
Miniature bottle of brandy

TREATING MINOR INJURIES

Burns and scalds should be cooled by holding the injured area in cold water or under a running tap for at least 10 minutes or until the pain subsides. If clothing over the burn can be removed easily take it off; otherwise place it in the cold water and once cooled, seek medical attention. If the burn is very large or deep, call for medical help immediately, especially if the victim is a baby or small child. If necessary, treat for shock (see below). Less serious burns, once cooled, should be covered with a sterilized dressing (not adhesive, which could stick to it). Do not apply greasy ointment or a fluffy dressing which could stick to the burn and increase the problem.

Blisters are best left uncovered so they can dry out and flake off. If the blister is likely to be knocked, cover it with clean dry dressing. Never prick a blister or try to peel it off.

Cuts should be carefully cleaned of any dirt, grit or foreign bodies. Wipe gently with gauze or sterilized cotton wool moistened in a little dilute disinfectant. Dry, and apply a suitable dressing. Do not apply antiseptic ointment as this can seal in germs. If the cut is sore and inflamed or exudes pus, see a doctor.

Bruises require a cold compress. Place a clean cloth or towel soaked in water on the injured spot or fill a plastic bag with ice cubes and hold it over the bruise. The flow of blood to the bruise (which is what makes it hurt) can be reduced if you are able to raise the injured part.

Choking in adults can be stopped by leaning them forward and striking firmly between the shoulder blades. If this does not work, stand behind the choking person and clasp arms around their chest at the level of the lowest ribs. Lean their head forward and push your hands upwards into the chest. Repeat until choking stops, or seek medical help. Use this method on children but apply only minimal pressure or, if they are small enough, lay them across your knee and slap hard between the shoulder blades. With babies support the chest and abdomen and smack gently between the shoulder blades.

Shock should be treated by loosening clothing and laying the casualty down. Raise the legs if possible and keep the casualty warm by covering with rugs or blankets. Do not supply a hot water bottle or turn on a fan heater. Moisten the casualty's lips with water but do not give a drink or offer alcohol. Check breathing and pulse constantly and summon medical help as soon as possible.

Nosebleeds can be stopped by leaning the victim forwards and pinching the nostrils together for about 10 minutes. If bleeding does not cease, apply an ice pack or cold compress to the nose.

Animal bites should be cleaned with water and covered with a dry, sterilized dressing. Ask a doctor to look at the wound as soon as possible.

Bee and wasp stings can be removed with tweezers, if visible to the eye. Otherwise, apply antihistamine cream to them. If whoever has been stung has an allergic reaction, take them to a doctor or hospital at once.

NAME	TELEPHONE NUMBER	WHEN OPEN
Doctor		
Casualty department		
Local chemist		
Late night chemist		
Vet		
Taxi/mini-cab		

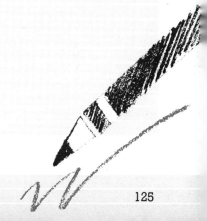

Coping with Emergencies

Even in the best and most organized homes, emergencies occur. People lose door keys, suddenly become ill or injure themselves, or a child may disappear, trees are struck by lightning, pipes burst, or you have a fire or flood.

In the space below you can fill in the telephone numbers and contacts suggested and add any others that might be helpful. Although a few of the same numbers may be recorded in other parts of your home log, it is sensible to keep them all together on this page and to spell out clearly what they are so that anyone can use the information. Bear in mind, too, that the friendly reliable plumber who normally does your repairs may not be on 24-hour call if you need him in the middle of the night. Make a separate note of any firm which specializes in emergencies such as clearing flood damage. Check details with emergency numbers before logging them here; when you are in a panic and need help quickly, you want to be sure it will come.

Tel. no.

Police

Fire brigade

Doctor

Nearest hospital
casualty department

Electricity board

Gas board

Water board

British Telecom

Local council

Plumber

Electrician

Locksmith

Glazier

Carpenter (new door)

House contents
insurance company

Taxi/mini-cab firm

Domestic help agency

Dentist

Optician/contact lens
supplier